PEEK-A-BOO PENGUIN
Sounds and Letters

Ruth Owen

Consultant: Jillian Harker

QED Publishing

Peek-a-boo Penguin arrives at nursery with Mummy Penguin.

He is wearing his **coat**.
He is holding his toy **boat**.
Coat and **boat** have the same sounds at the end. They **rhyme**.

Say the names of these things.

Can you find another thing in the big picture that **rhymes** with each of these?

Peek-a-boo is drawing on the blackboard.
Say the names of Peek-a-boo's pictures.

Match each picture to another
picture that **rhymes**.

Peek-a-boo is having fun at the toy **box**!
He is wearing a funny **wig**.
Can you find toys that **rhyme** with **box** and **wig**?

Say the names of the other toys.
Try matching the **rhyming sounds**.

Look at Peek-a-boo's flashcards.
Say what you see on the cards in each row.
Which card in each row **doesn't rhyme** with the others?

Funny Peek-a-boo is playing with the dressing-up box.
Say what you see in each row of Peek-a-boos.

Which word **doesn't rhyme** with
the other two in the row?

Today is dressing-up day at nursery.

Look at Peek-a-boo's friend Penny Penguin.
Penny is dressed as a **pirate**.

Can you spot Peek-a-boo?
What is Peek-a-boo dressed as?

Pirate and **panda** have the same
beginning sound.

Say the names of the children's costumes.

Match the costumes that have the same **beginning sound**.

Peek-a-boo is making a scrapbook with pictures of his favourite animals.

Try matching the animals that have the same **beginning sound**.

Now it's time for everyone to have a sleep.
Look at the pictures on the blankets.

Which picture in each row has a
different **beginning sound** to the other two?

Peek-a-boo has drawn some **pictures**.

The letter **p** writes the **beginning sound** in the word **pictures**.
Can you say what is in
Peek-a-boo's pictures?

i g l o o

t o m a t o

p i g

n e s t   **s** e a l

The letters that write the beginning sounds look like this.

i **t** **p** **n** **s**

Say what you see in each of these pictures.

t o r t o i s e

n u r s e

p e n g u i n

s u n

Can you match the **beginning sound** of each picture to one of these letters?

t   **p**   **n**   **s**

Peek-a-boo and Penny have been looking at books.
They have put some back on the shelves.

Say what the book on each shelf is about. Point to
the **letter** that writes the **beginning sound**.

Help Penny put these books on the shelves.

Say the name of each book. Point to the shelf
with the letter that writes the **beginning sound**.

It's time to tidy up!
Peek-a-boo and his friends must put
all the toys in the right toy box.

Look at the **letters** on the toy boxes.

d

c

t

18

Say the names of all the toys. Can you remember what the **beginning sound** of each toy looks like?

Help Peek-a-boo and his friends match each toy to the right toy box.

Peek-a-boo has some blocks with letters on them.

Try to say the **sound** that each **letter** makes.

Peek-a-boo has made a word with his blocks.

Can you sound out
each letter to make a word?

Peek-a-boo has made some more words.
Try sounding them out.

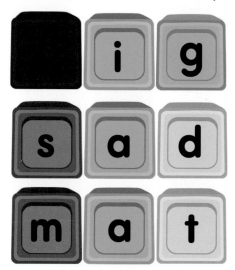

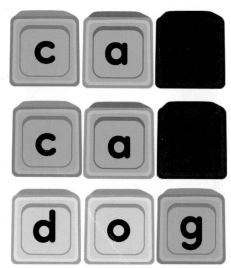

Can you help him to match each word to a reading card?

dog

can

pig

mat

cap

sad

More fun with Peek-a-boo!

Now look back through your book. Let's have some more fun with sounds and letters.

Peek-a-boo has drawn a **star**! Look for something in your book that **rhymes** with **star**.

Peek-a-boo is wearing a **hat**. Can you find some things in your book that **rhyme** with **hat**?

Peek-a-boo has
a toy **tiger**.
Find another toy with
the same **beginning
sound** as **tiger**.

Say the names of
Peek-a-boo's books.
Show Peek-a-boo which
bookshelf to put these books on.

Look at Peek-a-boo's blocks. Say the **sound** each
letter makes. Look for things in your book that begin
with each of these letters.

d

a

p

c

Notes for parents and teachers

The activities in this book are designed to encourage children to focus on the sounds in words and to introduce them to the idea that we use letters to represent these sounds – both important skills in learning to read and write. The emphasis is on making learning fun, by using an engaging character to capture and focus the interest of young children. The book will help children to recognize both rhyming and beginning sounds and also a range of letters that can be combined to make simple words.

Sit with the child and read each page to them. Allow time for the child to think about the activity. Encourage them to talk about what they are doing as they carry out the activity. Praise all attempts. If the child is hesitant, show the child how to begin by demonstrating the first part of the activity yourself.

Remember to keep activities short and to make them fun. Stop while your child is still interested. Avoid times when your child is tired or distracted and try another day. Children learn best when they are relaxed and enjoying themselves. It is best to help them to experience new concepts in small steps, rather than to do too much at once.

Use the book as a starting point for activities that your child could carry out at home or when out and about. Some ideas that you could try are:

- Play "Where's Peek-a-boo?" after each activity.

- Start a nursery rhyme but miss out some rhyming words. Ask your child to fill them in using either the correct word or any rhyming word to make a nonsense rhyme.

- Play rhyming "I spy", giving a word that rhymes with the object your child is to look for.

- Play a variation of "I spy" when you are out and about in places with plenty of sounds to focus on. Say, "I hear with my little ear something beginning with…" (do not give the name of the initial letter in the word, but give the beginning sound instead).

- Reinforce the letters introduced in the book by writing one on a piece of paper, clipping this to the side of a box and asking your child to put something in the box that begins with this letter.

Created by: Ruby Tuesday Books
Designer: Emma Randall

Copyright © QED Publishing 2011

First published in the UK in 2011 by
QED Publishing
A Quarto Group company
226 City Road
London EC1V 2TT

www.qed-publishing.co.uk

A catalogue record for this book is available from the British Library.

ISBN 978 1 84835 596 5

Printed in China

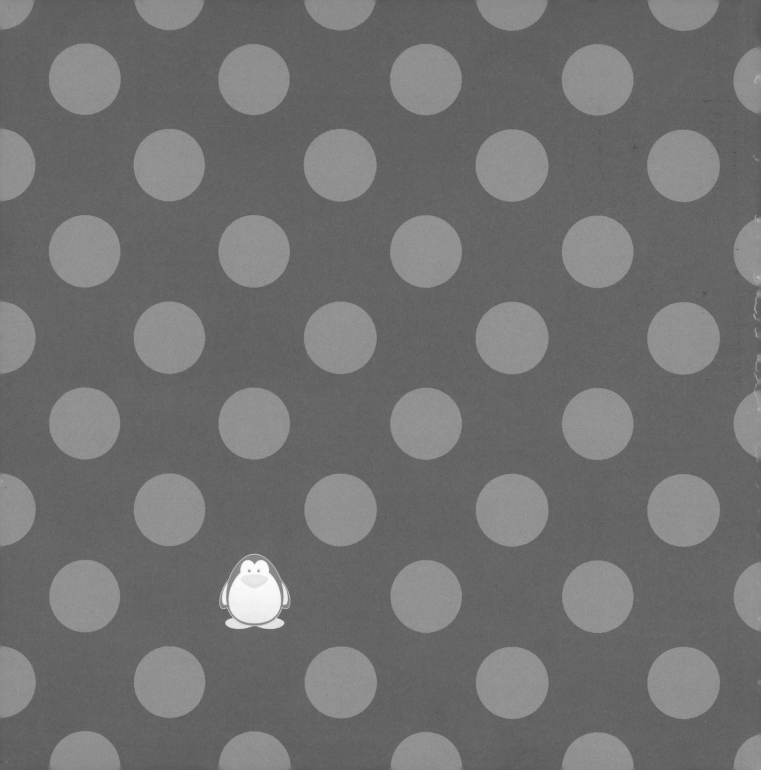